PICTURES BY JANINA DOMANSKA

WHAT DO YOU SEE?

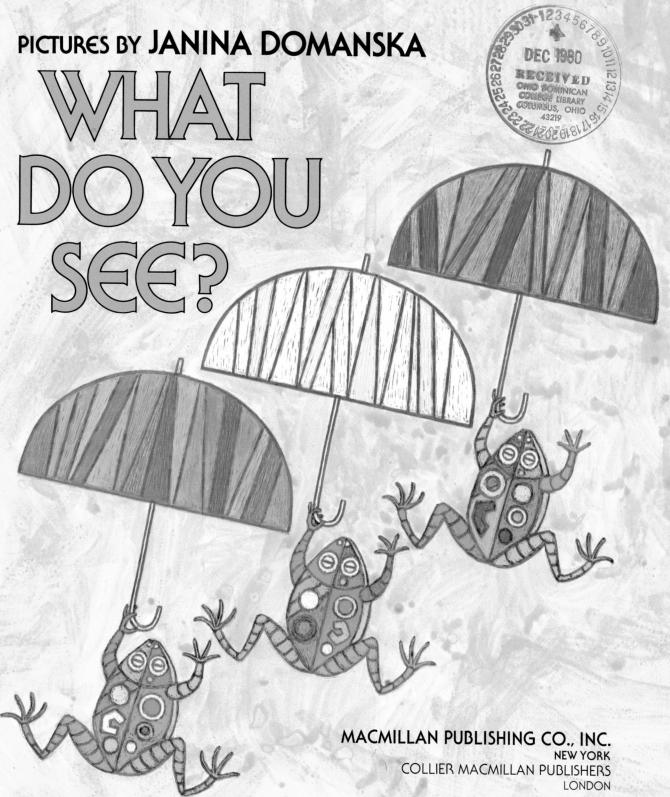

MACMILLAN PUBLISHING CO., INC.
NEW YORK
COLLIER MACMILLAN PUBLISHERS
LONDON

Macmillan Publishing Co., Inc., 866 Third Avenue, New York, N.Y. 10022 • Collier Macmillan
Canada Ltd. • Library of Congress catalog card number: 73–6052 • Printed in the United
States of America   2 3 4 5 6 7 8 9 10

The full-color artwork was done in aniline colors on scratchboard.
The typeface is Alphatype Serif Gothic.

Library of Congress Cataloging in Publication Data
Domanska, Janina.   What do you see? [1. Animals—Fiction. 2. Stories in rhyme] I. Title.
PZ8.3.D698Wh 811'.5'4 [E] 73–6052   ISBN 0-02-732830-9

112806

"What isn't water is mostly bog."

"Oh, not at all!" said the little fly.

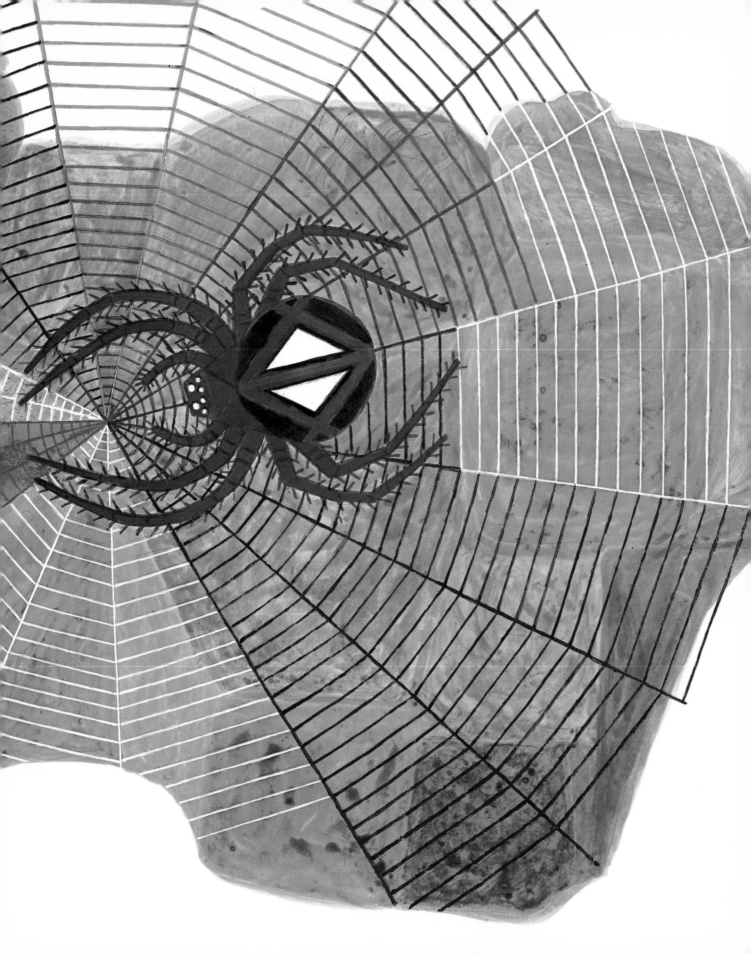

"It's full of spiders, and very dry!"

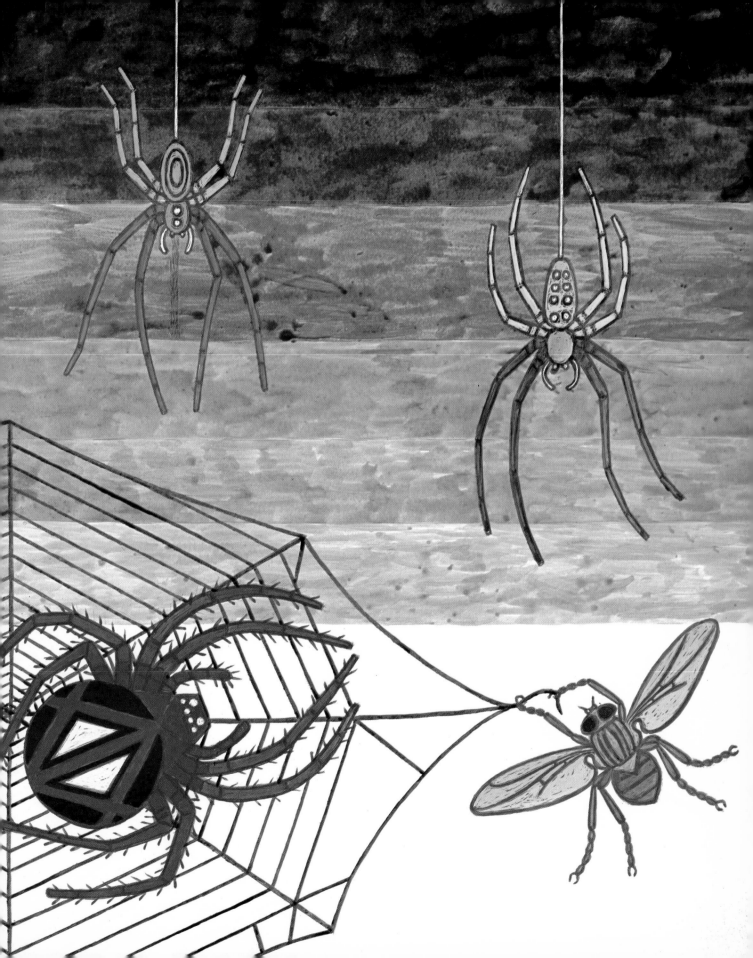

"The world is dark. I know I'm right,"
said the little bat who flies at night.

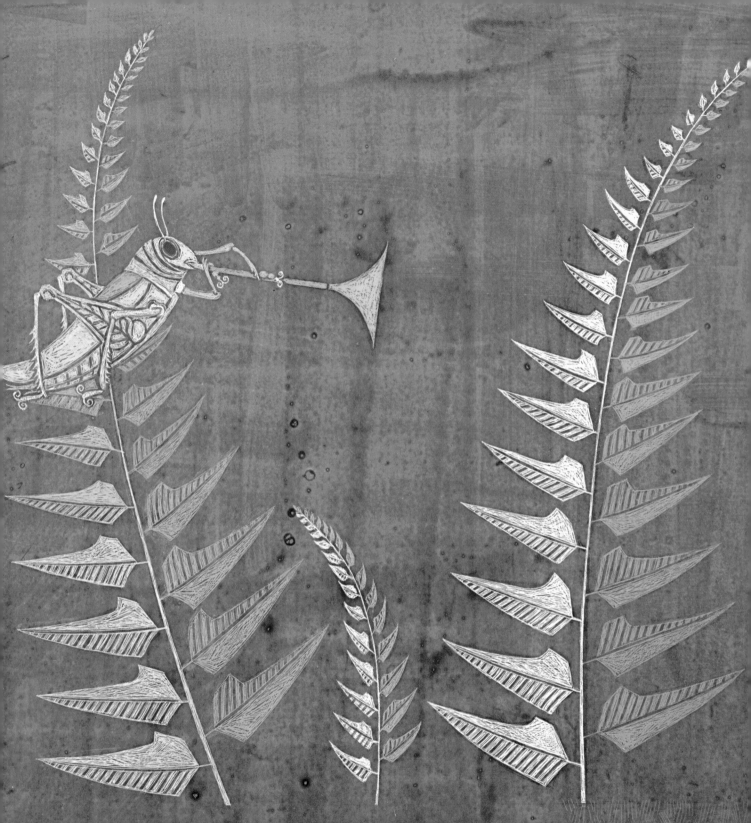

"It's clear to me you've much to learn.
The world is green," said the swaying fern.

"Oh, listen to me," sang the little lark.

"It's wet...

and dry...

and it's green

and dark.''